C000302272

Tom Kitten and His Friends

A play with songs

Book by Adrian Mitchell
Music by Stephen McNeff

Based on stories by Beatrix Potter

The Story of Miss Moppet
The Tale of Two Bad Mice
The Story of a Fierce Bad Rabbit
The Tale of Tom Kitten

Samuel French — London
New York - Toronto - Hollywood

© 1998 BY ADRIAN MITCHELL AND FREDERICK WARNE & CO.LTD

Rights of Performance by Amateurs are controlled by Samuel French Ltd, 52 Fitzroy Street, London W1P 6JR, and they, or their authorized agents, issue licences to amateurs on payment of a fee. **It is an infringement of the Copyright to give any performance or public reading of the play before the fee has been paid and the licence issued.**
The Royalty Fee for performance by Amateurs indicated below is subject to contract and subject to variation at the sole discretion of Samuel French Ltd.

        Basic fee for each and every
           performance of the play   Code G
           by amateurs in the British Isles

        Basic fee for each and every
           performance of the music   Code C
           by amateurs in the British Isles

Rights of Performance by Professionals are controlled by Peters Fraser and Dunlop, 503/4 The Chambers, Chelsea Harbour, London SW10 OXF.

All other rights are controlled by Frederick Warne & Co. Ltd, 27 Wrights Lane, London, W8 5TZ

Frederick Warne & Co. Ltd is the owner of all rights, copyrights and trademarks in the Beatrix Potter character names and illustrations. Permission to use any such illustrations must be obtained in advance from Frederick Warne & Co. Ltd.

The publication of this play does not imply that it is necessarily available for performance by amateurs or professionals, either in the British Isles or Overseas. Amateurs and professionals considering a production are strongly advised in their own interests to apply to the appropriate agents for consent before starting rehearsals or booking a theatre or hall.

The 23 Original Peter Rabbit Tales ™ by Beatrix Potter are published by Frederick Warne & Co. Ltd

ISBN 0 573 05116 X

Please see page iv for further copyright information

TOM KITTEN AND HIS FRIENDS

First performed at the Unicorn Theatre for Children,
London, on 23rd September, 1995, with the following
cast of characters:

Beatrix Potter	**Susan Webster**
Miss Moppet/Jane	**Billie-Claire Wright**
Tom Thumb/Jemima Puddle-Duck	**Adam Stafford**
Hunca Munca/Mittens	**Wendy Pitt**
Lucinda/Tabitha Twitchit	**Elsa O'Toole**
Fierce Bad Rabbit	**Marcello Marascalchi**
Nice Gentle Rabbit/Rebeccah Puddle-Duck	**Iain Jones**
Man With a Gun/Drake Puddle-Duck	**Paul Gilmore**
Appley Dapply/Tom Kitten	**Paul Ryan**

Directed by Richard Williams and Kieron Smith
Designed by David Collis
Lighting by Dave Horn
Musical Director Stephen McNeff

COPYRIGHT INFORMATION

(See also page ii)

This play is fully protected under the Copyright Laws of the British Common-wealth of Nations, the United States of America and all countries of the Berne and Universal Copyright Conventions.

All rights including Stage, Motion Picture, Radio, Television, Public Reading, and Translation into Foreign Languages, are strictly reserved.

No part of this publication may lawfully be reproduced in ANY form or by any means — photocopying, typescript, recording (including video-recording), manuscript, electronic, mechanical, or otherwise—or be transmitted or stored in a retrieval system, without prior permission.

Licences for amateur performances are issued subject to the understanding that it shall be made clear in all advertising matter that the audience will witness an amateur performance; that the names of the authors of the plays shall be included on all programmes; and that the integrity of the authors' work will be preserved.

The Royalty Fee is subject to contract and subject to variation at the sole discretion of Samuel French Ltd.

In Theatres or Halls seating Four Hundred or more the fee will be subject to negotiation.

In Territories Overseas the fee quoted above may not apply. A fee will be quoted on application to our local authorized agent, or if there is no such agent, on application to Samuel French Ltd, London.

VIDEO-RECORDING OF AMATEUR PRODUCTIONS

Please note that the copyright laws governing video-recording are extremely complex and that it should not be assumed that any play may be video-recorded for whatever purpose without first obtaining the permission of the appropriate agents. The fact that a play is published by Samuel French Ltd does not indicate that video rights are available or that Samuel French Ltd controls such rights.

CHARACTERS

Beatrix Potter
Miss Moppet, kitten
Mouse, hand puppet mouse
Tom Thumb, mouse
Hunca Munca, mouse
Lucinda, doll
Jane, doll
Fierce Bad Rabbit
Nice Gentle Rabbit
Man with a Gun
Mittens, kitten
Moppet, kitten
Tom Kitten
Tabitha Twitchit, kittens' mother
Drake Puddle-Duck
Rebeccah Puddle-Duck
Jemima Puddle-Duck
Three Friends of Tabitha

And a **Chorus of Animals**

The illustration used on the front cover is from *THE TALE OF TOM KITTEN* by Beatrix Potter.

Copyright © Frederick Warne & Co. Ltd, 1907, 1987. Reproduced by kind permission of Frederick Warne & Co.Ltd

Enquries regarding its use, for whatever purpose, must be addressed to Frederick Warne & Co Ltd, 27 Wrights Lane, London W8 5TZ.

SYNOPSIS OF SCENES

ACT I

Introduction

SCENE 1: The Story of Miss Moppet

Introduction

SCENE 2: The Tale of Two Bad Mice

ACT II

Introduction

SCENE 1: The Story of a Fierce Bad Rabbit

SCENE 2: The Tale of Tom Kitten

MUSICAL NUMBERS

ACT I

1.	**Appley Dapply 1**	Beatrix Potter
2.	**Scene Change Music**	
3.	**Mister Mouse 1**	Moppet
4.	**Appley Dapply 2**	Mouse
5.	**Mister Mouse 2**	Mouse and Moppet
6.	**Playing Catch**	Moppet
7.	**Appley Dapply (Reprise)**	Mouse
8.	**Playing Catch (Reprise)**	
9.	**The Old Woman**	Beatrix Potter and Company
10.	**Ninny Nanny Netticoat**	Beatrix Potter
11.	**Two Bad Mice**	Beatrix Potter and Company
12.	**Ninny Nanny Netticoat**	Beatrix Potter and Company

ACT II

13.	**We Have a Little Garden**	Company
14.	**We Have a Little Garden (Reprise)**	Beatrix Potter
15.	**Carrot of Mine**	Nice and Fierce
16.	**Man With a Gun**	Man With a Gun and Chorus
17.	**Carrot of Mine (Reprise)**	Nice
18.	**Kittens' Music**	
19.	**Scrubbing and Brushing**	Tabitha and Kittens
20.	**We Have a Little Garden**	Kittens
21.	**Pit Pat Paddle Pat**	Ducks
22.	**We Have a Little Garden**	Tabitha
23.	**Reprise of Songs**	Company

The music for this play, by Stephen McNeff, which is subject to a separate royalty fee, is available on hire from Samuel French Ltd.

PRODUCTION NOTES

The play is aimed at 3-5 year olds, so the actress playing Beatrix Potter must be ready to improvise, repeat, explain and deal with anything.

It is hoped that the play may sometimes be acted by a cast of young children with a teacher or adult friend in the part of Beatrix Potter.

For guidance on the appearance of puppet rabbit Benjamin, including costume, see the photograph which appears opposite page 52 of Judy Taylor's *Beatrix Potter, Artist, Storyteller and Country Woman*, published by Warne. Ideally Benjamin will be capable of moving along with her, of at least one simple head movement—a nod—to be controlled by Beatrix Potter through his lead. If this is not feasible, he can at least be pulled on small wheels, and when he is in her arms she can adjust his head.

In the score the song *Pit Pat Paddle Pat* shows how it was actually done at the Unicorn. The ducks came on to an extended *Pit Pat Paddle Pat*, went into *We are the Puddle-Ducks* and then introduced themselves while the others vamped in the background. The ducks then did a "straight" version of the song for their exit (this should be obvious between the score and the text). The version for the kittens on page 28 was very much *ad lib* (unaccompanied) in the manner of naughty children.

In *The Tale of Tom Kitten*, Tabitha's visiting friends can be doubled. Friend 1, for instance, could be played by the same actor as Nice Rabbit, Friend 2 by Doll Jane, Friend 3 by Tom Thumb.

This play is for Caitlin, Miranda, Zoe, Arthur and Lola

ACT I

CURTAIN *up on a young woman who will play Beatrix Potter. She is wearing modern everyday clothes and sitting at a piano*

Beatrix Potter (*playing and singing to the audience*) Once upon a time there was a woman called Beatrix Potter. Beatrix Potter loved to tell stories and sing songs about animals.

Appley Dapply 1
Appley Dapply, a little brown mouse
Goes to the cupboard in somebody's house
Appley Dapply has sharp little eyes,
And Appley Dapply is so fond of pies!

In somebody's cupboard
There's everything nice,
Cake, cheese, jam, biscuits—
All charming for mice!

Appley Dapply has sharp little eyes,
And Appley Dapply is so fond of pies!

She gets up from the piano and approaches the audience, carrying a wicker basket which she puts down on the stage. She addresses the audience

I'm going to pretend to be Beatrix Potter. So I'd better dress up in clothes like the ones she used to wear. (*She opens the wicker basket and takes out a long skirt*) She used to wear a long skirt like this. (*She puts on the skirt*) And it fastens round here. And she used to wear a dark velvety jacket. (*She takes out a jacket and puts it on, stroking it*) It was very smooth and soft, like a mole or a puppy dog. And it does up down the front. (*She takes a hat out of the basket*) And on top of her head, she wore a—hat.

She pauses, allowing the audience to tell her that a hat is the best thing to wear on her head

And her hat had bows at the back, like little wings. And all around the front of her hat, little flowers were growing. (*She puts the hat on*) Good. I am Miss Beatrix Potter. Every morning I like to walk in my garden. But it's lonely walking without my best friend Benjamin. I wonder where he is. (*She looks around*) Benjamin! Where are you?

The lid of the basket tips half open and closes again

Benjamin!

The lid tips again. The audience should now be reacting. Beatrix Potter sees and kneels down to the basket

There you are! Don't be shy, Benjamin. Come out and meet lots of new friends. Come on.

She lifts out a rabbit, Benjamin. She stands with him in her arms. He has a collar and a light lead

This is my friend Mr Benjamin Bunny. Benjamin, these are our new friends. Yes, you may get down. (*She puts him on the ground still on his lead*) Every morning I take Mr Benjamin Bunny on his lead to the edge of our cabbage bed for his breakfast. He loves cabbage for breakfast. My father once gave him sweets. They were peppermints. Benjamin liked them. He gobbled them all up. But he munched them instead of sucking them. So he had a toothache and his face was all swollen. I made him better again with cuddling and cabbage and lots of stories. Would you like a story now?

Benjamin nods

All right, I'll tell you a story about a kitten. She was very young and pretty and a most fearful pickle. And her name was Miss Moppet. So this is…

THE STORY OF MISS MOPPET

The Lights change. Scene change music

Beatrix Potter resumes her seat at the piano and plays. Back curtains part to reveal an old-fashioned drawing room. There is a cupboard, a fireplace with a bell-pull beside it, and a cushion in front of it. In front of the fire, facing us, sits Miss Moppet. She is a tabby kitten with a pink bow. She is played by an actress in costume. The mouse in the story is a hand-puppet worked and voiced by an actor

Beatrix Potter This is a pussy called Miss Moppet.
Moppet Shhhhhh! I think I have heard a mouse! Shhhhhh!

*Mouse looks out from behind the cupboard. He wears a green jacket and
a pink bow-tie*

Mouse You did hear a mouse and I am that mouse and I am not afraid of a
kitten. Shall I sing you a song, Miss Moppet?
Moppet No, Mister Mouse, I will sing you a song.

Mister Mouse 1
Mister Mouse, Mister Mouse
Hurry out of my house!
Mister Mouse, Mister Mouse
Scurry out of my house!

Scoot away, shoot away
Leave my happy household!
Hide away, slide away
To your secret mousehole!

Mister Mouse, Mister Mouse
Hurry out of my house!
Mister Mouse, Mister Mouse
Scurry out of my house!

Scoot away, shoot away
Leave my happy household!
Hide away, slide away
To your secret mousehole!

Mouse Miss Moppet—stop it! Miss Moppet—stop it!
I don't like your song, I'll sing you a better one.
(*To the audience*) I love to make fun of Miss Moppet.

*Mouse emerges from behind the cupboard to sing and dance very boldly to
Miss Moppet, who gradually, during the song, prepares to spring upon the
Mouse*

Appley Dapply 2
Appley Dapply, a little brown mouse
Goes to the cupboard in somebody's house
Appley Dapply has sharp little eyes,
And Appley Dapply is so fond of pies!

> In somebody's cupboard
> There's everything nice
> Cake, cheese, jam, biscuits,
> All charming for mice!
>
> Appley Dapply has sharp little eyes,
> And Appley Dapply is so fond of pies!

Miss Moppet springs. Just too late, she misses the Mouse and hits her nose on the cupboard

Moppet Just too late! Just too late!
   I missed Mister Mouse and hit my poor nose.
   I think that is a very hard cupboard. (*She strokes her nose to make it better and sings*)

Mister Mouse 2
Mister Mouse, Mister Mouse
Hurry out of my house!
Mister Mouse, Mister Mouse
Scurry out of my house!

Chorus   Scoot away, shoot away
               Leave my happy household!
               Hide away, slide away
               To your secret mousehole!

The cupboard doors open and Mouse appears

Mouse   I'm a brave little mouse
               And I'm safe in your house!
               I'm a brave little mouse
               I'm happy in your house!

Moppet   Scoot away, shoot away
               Leave my happy household!
               Hide away, slide away
               To your secret mousehole!

Moppet leaps at him again, but once more the Mouse is too quick and she hits her head on the closing cupboard door

Moppet Just too late! Just too late!
   I missed Mister Mouse again and hit my poor head. (*She rubs her head to make it better*)

How can I catch that naughty Mister Mouse?
I know, I'll play a trick on him.
A clever trick, for I'm a clever kitten.
I'll pretend that the cupboard hurt my head very badly
and I'm very ill. I'll use this duster for a head bandage. (*She ties a huge blue and white duster around her head*)
Oh, my poor head, I think I'll sit before the fire until it's better. (*She climbs on the cushion in front of the fire*)

The Mouse looks at her from high behind the cupboard

Mouse Oh dear, Miss Moppet's looking very ill.
I'd better go down for a closer look.
I'll climb down this bell-pull. (*He climbs down cautiously. He inspects Miss Moppet from a safe distance*)
Moppet Oh my poor nose! Oh my poor head!
Oh my poor tail and whiskers!
Mouse She looks worse and worse.
I'll go a little closer.

Miss Moppet holds her head in her paws. She looks at the mouse through a hole in the duster

Beatrix Potter She was pretending to be ill. But she was watching the mouse through a hole in the duster.
Moppet Oh my poor nose! Oh my poor head!
Oh my poor tail and whiskers!
Mouse Oh Miss Moppet, are you very ill and pale?
Moppet Oh Mister Mouse, I'm not too ill—to catch you by the tail!

Moppet jumps and catches the Mouse

If mice tease kittens, kittens will tease mice!
Mouse Oh Miss Moppet, that's not very nice!
Miss Moppet—stop it! Miss Moppet—stop it!

Moppet takes the duster from her head, ties the Mouse up in it and tosses it about like a ball

Playing Catch
Moppet   For a kitten the greatest fun of all
Is playing catch with a mouse in a ball
For a kitten the greatest fun of all
Is playing catch with a mouse in a ball

Send him flying and watch him spin and fall
It's such good sport with a mouse in a ball
Send him flying and watch him spin and fall
It's such good sport with a mouse in a ball.

Beatrix Potter But Miss Moppet forgot about that hole in the duster.

Moppet unties the duster

So when she untied it—there was no mouse!
Moppet No mouse!
Beatrix Potter He has wriggled out and run away. And look! He is dancing
a jig on the cupboard!

Mouse	**Appley Dapply (Reprise)**

Appley Dapply (Reprise)
Appley Dapply, a little brown mouse
Goes to the cupboard in somebody's house
Appley Dapply has sharp little eyes,
And Appley Dapply is so fond of pies!

In somebody's cupboard
There's everything nice,
Cake, cheese, jam, biscuits—
All charming for mice!

Appley Dapply has sharp little eyes,
And Appley Dapply is so fond of pies!

Miss Moppet looks very disgruntled

Beatrix Potter And that is the end of the story of Miss Moppet.

Playing Catch (Reprise)
For a kitten the greatest fun of all
Is playing catch with a mouse in a ball
For a kitten the greatest fun of all
Is playing catch with a mouse in a ball

Send him flying and watch him spin and fall
It's such good sport with a mouse in a ball
Send him flying and watch him spin and fall
It's such good sport with a mouse in a ball

Mouse bows and Miss Moppet curtsies and Beatrix Potter leads the applause.

Back curtains close on the drawing-room set. Beatrix Potter sits at her piano and plays

The Old Woman

Beatrix Potter   You know the old woman who lives in a shoe?
Had so many children
She didn't know what to do?
I think if she lived in a little shoe house
That little old woman was surely a mouse!

Company   You know the old woman who lives in a shoe?
Had so many children
She didn't know what to do?
I think if she lived in a little shoe house
That little old woman was surely a mouse!

Beatrix Potter   We're counting the children who live in the shoe
A line of children
Which stretches to Timbuktu
There's seventy-leven! there's fourtleby-two!
There's so many children so what can we do?

Company   We're counting the children who live in the shoe
A line of children
Which stretches to Timbuktu
There's seventy-leven! there's fourtleby-two!
There's so many children so what can we do?

You know the old woman who lives in a shoe?
Had so many children
She didn't know what to do?
I think if she lived in a little shoe house
That little old woman was surely a mouse!

Beatrix Potter (*speaking*) I once knew two mice called Tom Thumb and Hunca Munca. They were caught in a kitchen in Gloucestershire. I had a little house built for them. Watching them carry treasures into their nest gave me the idea for the next story. And the story is called...

THE TALE OF TWO BAD MICE

Beatrix Potter (*playing the piano*) Once upon a time there was a very beautiful doll's house.

*An Assistant carries on a doll's house as in the first illustration of the story.
The Assistant places doll Jane on the roof and doll Lucinda on the floor in
front of the doll's house, which is sited downstage at one side of the stage*

Thank you.

The Assistant exits

(*Still playing the piano*) The doll's house was red brick with white
windows, and it had real muslin curtains and a front door and a chimney.
That's a lovely doll's house, but it's rather small for our story. May we have
a bigger one please?

*Piano. Change of Lighting. Curtains part. There is a much bigger doll's
house, big enough, in fact, for actors to enter and even climb the stairs. There
is also a large doll's pram at the side of the stage, big enough for people to
climb in. But the pram's handle is just out of sight off stage*

As I was saying, once upon a time there was a very beautiful doll's house;
it was red brick with white windows and it had real muslin curtains and a
front door and a chimney. It belonged to two dolls called Lucinda and Jane.

*Lucinda enters, a doll who has blonde hair with a blue ribbon and a long
blue dress with puffed sleeves*

Lucinda I am Lucinda and the house belongs to me. But I never order meals
because I am a doll.

Jane enters, a wooden doll with a pink frock, white apron and dark hair

Jane I am Jane and I am the cook. But I never do any cooking, because the
dinner had been bought ready-made in a box full of shavings.
Lucinda (*to the audience*) Would you like to see our doll's house food?

The audience: "Yes!"

Good. Jane, will you help me to open the house?
Jane You mean the front door, ma'am?
Lucinda No, Jane, I mean the front wall.

*The front wall of the doll's house is on hinges, and Jane and Lucinda heave
it open. In the kitchen is a large box marked "provisions"*

Now let's open up the box and show everybody our doll's house food.

Jane Certainly, Miss Lucinda. (*She opens the box, which is full of wood shavings and produces dishes, one by one, showing them proudly to the audience. First there are two red lobsters, then as described*)
Lucinda A ham.
Jane A fish.
Lucinda A pudding.
Jane And some pears and oranges.
Lucinda None of them will come off the plates…
Jane But they are extremely beautiful.

All the dishes are now on the kitchen table

Lucinda We have been invited out this evening to my friend Polly's doll's house.
Jane It will be lovely to look at her food. What time shall we go?
Lucinda We are invited for six o'clock.

The clock strikes six

  Six o'clock!
Jane We had better drive round in the perambulator.
Lucinda Certainly.

Lucinda and Jane clamber into the perambulator and settle down

  What a beautiful evening!

The Lights are lowered somewhat

Jane And just look at the moon and stars.

The moon and stars come out

Lucinda To Miss Polly's if you please!

An invisible little girl pulls the pram off stage and we hear it rumbling off

Beatrix Potter And so Lucinda and Jane rode off to their friend's house to look at dinner. And it was time to light the candles. (*She stands and lights the candles which stand in the brackets above the keyboard of the piano*) I'll sing a song about a candle.

Ninny Nanny Netticoat
Ninny Nanny Netticoat

> In a white petticoat
> With a red nose,
> With a red nose,
> The longer she stands,
> The shorter she grows.

(*Speaking*) It's a riddle song.

> Ninny Nanny Netticoat
> In a white petticoat
> With a red nose,
> With a red nose,
> The longer she stands,
> The shorter she grows.

(*Speaking*) Did you get it?
The answer to the riddle is—a candle!

> Ninny Nanny Netticoat
> In a white petticoat
> With a red nose,
> With a red nose,
> The longer she stands,
> The shorter she grows.

> Ninny Nanny Netticoat
> In a white petticoat
> With a red nose,
> With a red nose,
> The longer she stands,
> The shorter she grows.

Now it was very quiet in the doll's house that evening. Very, very quiet.
But we can hear a little scuffling, scratching noise in the corner near the
fireplace where there was a mousehole. It was Tom Thumb.

*Tom Thumb, a mouse played by an actor rather than a glove puppet, puts
his head out of the hole for a moment, then pops it in again. Then he puts
it out of the hole*

Tom Thumb Yes, that's me—Tom Thumb.

Hunca Munca, another mouse, puts her head out of the hole

Hunca Munca And I'm his wife, Hunca Munca. Shall we go out, Tom Thumb?

Tom Thumb Yes, there's no-one about, Hunca Munca.

Hunca Munca Better go cautiously, better be slow.

Tom Thumb There might be somebody—you never know.

The two mice carefully scout around the stage and converge at the doll's house

Hunca Munca Perhaps there's somebody there asleep.

Tom Thumb We'll just pop in and take a peep.

Hunca Munca \
Tom Thumb | (*together*) Yes, we'll just pop in and take a peep.

They do, and they squeak with joy to find the table laid with all those dishes

Hunca Munca Such a lovely dinner laid out upon the table!

Tom Thumb They've left us tin spoons, and lead knives and forks——

Hunca Munca And two dolly-chairs—all so convenient!

The mice climb up on the chairs and Tom Thumb takes a knife and fork to the ham

Tom Thumb I'll carve the ham.

Hunca Munca It's beautiful shiny yellow ham, all streaked with red.

But the knife crumples up on Tom Thumb's hand. He puts his finger in his mouth

Tom Thumb Ouch! The ham is not boiled enough. It is hard. You have a try, Hunca Munca.

Hunca Munca stands on her chair and chops at the ham with another lead knife

Hunca Munca It's as hard as the hams at the cheesemonger's.

The ham breaks off the plate and rolls under the table

Tom Thumb Let it alone. Give me some fish, Hunca Munca.

Hunca Munca tries to lever the fish off its plate with a tin spoon

Hunca Munca It's no good, Tom Thumb. The fish is glued to the dish!

Tom Thumb (*in a mounting fury*) The fish is glued to the dish! The fish is glued to the dish!

Beatrix Potter Then Tom Thumb lost his temper.

Tom Thumb puts the ham in the middle of the floor and hits it with the fire-tongs and the shovel—bang, bang, smash, smash! The ham breaks up

The ham flew all into pieces, for underneath the shiny paint it was made of nothing but plaster! Then there was no end to the rage and disappointment of Tom Thumb and Hunca Munca.

Tom Thumb and Hunca Munca break up the pudding, lobsters, the pears and the oranges

Two Bad Mice
Two bad mice
Two bad mice
See how they run!
See how they run!
They like to visit you in the night
And try to eat everything in sight
And steal your playthings by candlelight
Those two bad, two bad mice.

Hunca Munca The fish still won't come off the plate!

Tom Thumb Let's burn it in the red-hot kitchen fire.

They attempt this

Beatrix Potter But the fish would not burn in the red-hot crinkly paper fire.

The mice rush around the doll's house causing havoc. Tom Thumb—if possible—looks out of the top of the chimney. Hunca Munca finds some canisters

Hunca Munca Food! I've found some food! Tins and tins of it.

Tom Thumb What's in the tins?

Hunca Munca (*reading the labels*) Rice—coffee—sago—currants. (*She starts to empty them out*) Beads! Nothing but red and blue beads!

Two bad mice
Two bad mice
They're having fun
They're having fun

> They break the food, throw it on the ground
> There's coloured beads rolling round and round
> They're turning the whole house upside-down
> Those two bad, two bad mice.

Tom Thumb That's the last straw! Let's do all the mischief we can. (*He takes Jane's clothes out of a chest of drawers and throws them out of the window*)

> Two bad mice
> Two bad mice
> What have they done?
> What have they done?
> They've broken everything they can break
> They've taken everything they can take
> Made all the mischief that they can make
> Those two bad, two bad mice.

Hunca Munca Come and help me, Tom Thumb. There's a bolster here which could make us an excellent feather bed.

The mice manage to push and pull the bolster down the stairs and over to the mousehole

Tom Thumb It'll never go in.
Hunca Munca We'll manage somehow.

The bolster goes in. The mice run back and fetch a book, a birdcage, an iron and a looking-glass

Beatrix Potter   (*singing*) Two bad mice
> Two bad mice
> See how they run!
> See how they run!
> They like to visit you in the night
> And try to eat everything in sight
> And steal your playthings by candlelight
> Those two bad, two bad mice.

> Two bad mice
> Two bad mice
> See how they run!
> See how they run!
> They like to visit you in the night

> And try to eat everything in sight
> And steal your playthings by candlelight
> Those two bad, two bad mice.

Tom Thumb The bookcase and the birdcage won't go into our mousehole.
Hunca Munca Leave them behind the coal-box. Come and help me fetch
a cradle for our babies.

> Two bad mice
> Two bad mice
> See how they run!
> See how they run!
> They like to visit you in the night
> And try to eat everything in sight
> And steal your playthings by candlelight
> Those two bad, two bad mice.

The mice fetch the cradle which is on rockers, and goes in the mousehole

> *But just as they are stealing a chair, coverlet and a broom, the end of the
> doll's pram appears, bearing an indignant Lucinda and Jane*

> *The Mice rush into their hole*

The dolls clamber from their pram, enter the house and inspect the damage

Beatrix Potter What a sight met the eyes of Jane and Lucinda! Lucinda sat
upon the upset kitchen table and stared. And Jane leant against the kitchen
dresser and smiled—but neither of them made any remark.

The dolls take up this pose

Jane Least said, soonest mended, Miss Lucinda.
Lucinda That's right, Jane. It's Christmas Eve and we should be in bed.

*The dolls go upstairs, hang stockings on the end of their bed and pop into bed,
still wearing their clothes*

Beatrix Potter But the Two Bad Mice were not so very naughty after all,
because Tom Thumb paid for everything he broke.

> *Tom Thumb climbs the doll's house stairs carrying sixpence and puts it in
> a stocking as the dolls watch him secretly*

He found a crooked sixpence by the hearth and on that Christmas Eve, he stuffed it into one of the stockings of Lucinda and Jane. And very early every morning—before anybody is awake—he and Hunca Munca come with their dust-pan and broom to sweep the dolls' house! And every night Lucinda and Jane hear Hunca Munca singing this lullaby to her children.

The wall around the mousehole becomes transparent and we see Hunca Munca sitting with one baby mouse on her lap and three more in the cradle. Model mice, not actors

Ninny Nanny Netticoat
Ninny Nanny Netticoat,
In a white petticoat
With a red nose,
With a red nose,
The longer she stands,
The shorter she grows.

And that is the Tale of the Two Bad Mice. So I've told you the stories of the Two Bad Mice and Miss Moppet. We're going to have an interval now, so that you can talk and have drinks or ices and go to the lavatory. And if you'll come back in about fifteen minutes you shall meet Benjamin again and we will tell you the story of a Fierce Bad Rabbit and The Tale of Tom Kitten.

Company   Ninny Nanny Netticoat
In a white petticoat
With a red nose,
With a red nose,
The longer she stands,
The shorter she grows.

Ninny Nanny Netticoat
In a white petticoat
With a red nose,
With a red nose,
The longer she stands,
The shorter she grows.

Beatrix Potter plays the piano. The house Lights come up

Curtain

ACT II

Beatrix Potter is at the piano. She wears the hat, velvet top and long skirt as in Act I. She starts to play

Company

We Have a Little Garden

We have a little garden
A garden of our own
And every day we water there
The seeds that we have sown

We love our little garden
And tend it with such care
You will not find a faded leaf
Or blighted blossom there

We have a little garden
A garden of our own
And every day we water there
The seeds that we have sown

We love our little garden
And tend it with such care
You will not find a faded leaf
Or blighted blossom there

Bright snowdrops in the winter
And Christmas roses there
Then springtime brings the crocuses
To sniff the April air

The pears and apples shining
They cheer us in the fall
But strawberries mean summertime
The sweetest time of all.

Something is wrong with the high notes. She inspects the keyboard. She starts again. Double-takes on its contents. She takes from inside the piano the rabbit Benjamin, and looks at him sternly

Beatrix Potter Benjamin Bouncer! That is a piano not a rabbit hutch! (*She shuts the lid and stands Benjamin on top of the piano*) Mr Benjamin Bunny and I had an adventure this morning. I took him to the edge of the cabbage bed with his leather dog-lead. I heard a rustling, and out came a little wild rabbit to talk to him. It crept half-way across the cabbage bed, then sat up on its hind legs grunting. I replied with grunts. (*She does a couple of grunts to show how to address a rabbit*) But stupid Benjamin did nothing but stuff himself with cabbage. The other rabbit was a female, and of a shabby appearance. She advanced with her face twitching with excitement and admiration for the beautiful Benjamin. But when he peeped round a cabbage and saw her, he turned and bolted. He probably thought she was a cat. I caught him and comforted him and we sang our garden song.

We Have a Little Garden (Reprise)
> Our greenhouse is a palace
> Our lawn as soft as silk
> And if a hedgehog comes to call
> We feed him bread and milk
>
> We picnic with the daisies
> Why don't you come and see?
> We'll let you use the garden hose
> And climb the apple tree.

She teaches the audience the song line by line then she sings it with them

Now Benjamin says it's time for a story. I made up this story for a little girl who told me that she thought Peter Rabbit was much too good and she wanted a story about a really naughty rabbit; so this is...

THE STORY OF A FIERCE BAD RABBIT

Back curtains part to reveal a green bench, and, far behind it, painted trees

Fierce Bad Rabbit enters. An actor, not a puppet

Fierce bad music

Fierce I am Fierce Bad Rabbit. Look at my savage whiskers. Look at my sharp little claws. Look at my very handsome turned-up tail. I have had no breakfast today, so I am especially fierce and bad.

Fierce Bad Rabbit exits

Nice Gentle Rabbit enters with a carrot. He climbs on to the bench

Nice I am a nice gentle rabbit. My mother has given me a carrot.

Carrot of Mine
Carrot so crunchy
And orangey red
Carrot from somebody's
Vegetable bed!

Carrot so juicy
Carrot so fine,
Oh, how I love you
Carrot of mine!

Carrot so crunchy
And orangey red
Carrot from somebody's
Vegetable bed!

Carrot so juicy
Carrot so fine,
Oh, how I love you
Carrot of mine!

Nice begins to munch

Fierce enters

He sees the carrot and stalks Nice, catching him unawares as he leaps on to the bench

Fierce I am a Fierce Bad Rabbit and I would like some carrot.
Nice Say "please", Fierce Bad Rabbit.
Fierce I never say please. If I want it, I take it—for I am a Fierce Bad Rabbit.

Fierce pushes Nice, Nice falls off the bench, leaving the carrot on the bench. Fierce chases Nice, scratching him

Nice You scratched me badly, you Fierce Bad Rabbit. (*To the audience*) I will creep away and hide in a hole. I feel sad. (*He hides in a hole—still visible—at the side of the stage*)

Fierce mounts the bench and begins to chew the carrot

Fierce   Carrot so crunchy
                              And orangey red
                              Carrot from somebody's
                              Vegetable bed!

                              Carrot so juicy
                              Carrot so fine,
                              Oh, how I love you
                              Carrot of mine!

                              Carrot so crunchy
                              And orangey red
                              Carrot from somebody's
                              Vegetable bed!

                              Carrot so juicy
                              Carrot so fine,
                              Oh, how I love you
                              Carrot of mine!

Far at the back of the stage, Man with a Gun enters. He wears a green hat and jacket, brown knickerbockers, yellow boots and a bag for game slung over his shoulder. He has a ginger beard and a shotgun under his arm

Man With a Gun

Man   I am a man with a gun gun gun
                              I think shooting animals is fun fun fun
                              If I heard a robin that sang sang sang
                              I'd stop his singing with my bang bang bang
                              For I think shooting animals is fun fun fun
                              And I am the man with the gun gun gun
                              Yes I am a man with a gun

Chorus   I am a man with a gun gun gun
                              I think shooting animals is fun fun fun
                              If I heard a robin that sang sang sang
                              I'd stop his singing with my bang bang bang
                              For I think shooting animals is fun fun fun
                              And I am a man with a gun gun gun
                              Yes I am a man with a gun

Man   I am a man and I'm strong and tall
                              And I'll bully anyone who's weak or small
                              When I see an eagle that's in full flight

Or badgers dancing in the bright moonlight
I raise my hunting rifle up and down they fall
For I am a man and I'm strong and tall
Yes I'm very strong and I'm tall

Chorus

I am a man with a gun gun gun
I think shooting animals is fun fun fun
If I heard a robin that sang sang sang
I'd stop his singing with my bang bang bang
For I think shooting animals is fun fun fun
And I am a man with a gun gun gun
Yes I am a man with a gun

Man

Look at my gun see it shine, shine, shine
And look at these fields and woods they're mine all
    mine
If I catch you walking your dog today
I'll fire my gun and chase you both away
So keep out of these fields and woods they're mine
    all mine
And look at my gun see it shine, shine, shine
Yes look at my gun see it shine

Chorus

I am a man with a gun gun gun
I think shooting animals is fun fun fun
If I heard a robin that sang sang sang
I'd stop his singing with my bang bang bang
For I think shooting animals is fun fun fun
And I am a man with a gun gun gun
Yes I am a man with a gun

Man

I am a man with a gun gun gun
I get hot and angry in the noonday sun
I paid for this countryside it's just for me
I don't want animals for company
But I can scare them easily and off they run
For I am a man with a gun gun gun
Yes I am a man with a gun

Chorus

I am a man with a gun gun gun
I think shooting animals is fun fun fun
If I heard a robin that sang sang sang
I'd stop his singing with my bang bang bang
For I think shooting animals is fun fun fun

> And I am a man with a gun gun gun
> Yes I am a man with a gun.

What's that? What's that I see? I see something. Something sitting. Something sitting on a bench. What's that? What's that I see? I think it is a very funny bird! Time for some fun. Fun with my gun.

Man creeps towards Fierce Bad Rabbit, who begins to realize something is wrong. Man levels the gun

Goodbye funny bird!

BANG! The bang shouldn't be too violent, but there should be a wild lighting effect, during which the Fierce Bad Rabbit disappears off the bench with a howl, leaving the carrot, his tail and his whiskers on the bench

Beatrix Potter steps forward

Beatrix Potter The Fierce Bad Rabbit ran away.

Man approaches the bench

And all the man found on the bench was——

As he speaks, the Man displays the pathetic trophies

Man
Beatrix } (*together*) A carrot. A rabbit's tail. And some savage whiskers.

The Man trudges off home

Nice Rabbit peeps out of its hole

Fierce Bad Rabbit comes limping past

Nice Fierce Bad Rabbit! Fierce Bad Rabbit! Where is your very handsome turned-up tail? Where are your savage whiskers?

Carrot of Mine (Reprise)
Carrot so crunchy
And orangey red
Carrot from somebody's
Vegetable bed!

> Carrot so juicy
> Carrot so fine,
> Oh, how I love you
> Carrot of mine!
>
> Carrot so crunchy
> And orangey red
> Carrot from somebody's
> Vegetable bed!
>
> Carrot so juicy
> Carrot so fine,
> Oh, how I love you
> Carrot of mine!

Fierce does not answer, but limps off

The back curtains close

Beatrix Potter And that is the end of the Story of a Fierce Bad Rabbit. I love all sorts of animals. My little brother Bertram and I lived in London. But we used to bring back animals from holidays in the country or buy them in London pet shops. We had a green frog called Punch and two lizards called Toby and Judy. There were some water newts and Sally, a very pretty ring-snake. Later I grew to love collie dogs and sheep. And of course rabbits (*to Benjamin*) were always special. But for my last story today, I would like to tell you about a family of cats. So listen now to…

The Tale of Tom Kitten

Mittens, a female cat, and Tom Kitten enter

Mittens I am Mittens.
Tom I am Tom Kitten.
Moppet I am Miss Moppet. We have met before.
Beatrix Potter They had dear little fur coats of their own; and they tumbled about the doorstep and played in the dust.

Kittens' Music

The Kittens spring into action and play boisterously, wrestling, pushing and jumping out at each other with music. Not too long, or the audience will start

*to join in. Should they do so, Beatrix Potter should ask them to resume their
seats on the grounds that they are not kittens*

One day their mother, Mrs Tabitha Twitchit, expected friends to tea.

Suddenly, Mrs Tabitha Twitchit comes out of the house

Tabitha Stop playing, Kittens! Tom and Mittens! Stop it, Moppet!
Kittens Why, why can't we play? It's such a lovely summer day.
Tabitha I am expecting friends to tea. So come indoors immediately. I must
wash and dress each one of you before the fine company arrives.

*Tabitha chases kittens indoors. There is a wash basin, towels, a sponge,
brush, comb and an assortment of clothes*

Mittens Why do we have to be washed, mama?
Tom Why do we have to be brushed, mama?
Moppet Why do we have to wear clothes, mama?
Tabitha So my visitors say: What fine kittens you are! (*She sings as she
scrubs Moppet's face with a sponge*)

Scrubbing and Brushing
Take a soggy scrubby sponge
To that grubby face of yours
Take a soggy scrubby sponge
To those muddy muddy paws.

Take a soggy scrubby sponge
To that grubby face of yours
Take a soggy scrubby sponge
To those muddy muddy paws.

Moppet

That's enough Mama
You're too rough Mama
That's enough Mama
Oh no more no more

That's enough Mama
You're too rough Mama
That's enough Mama
Oh no more no more.

Tabitha

(*brushing Mittens*) Take a bristly little brush

To that dusty cat of mine
Take a bristly little brush
Till her fur begins to shine.

Take a bristly little brush
To that dusty cat of mine
Take a bristly little brush
Till her fur begins to shine.

Mittens   (*singing*) That's enough Mama
You're too rough Mama
That's enough Mama
Now my fur's all sore

That's enough Mama
You're too rough Mama
That's enough Mama
Now my fur's all sore.

Tabitha   (*combing Tom*) Take a spiky little comb
To your whiskers and your tail
Take a spiky little comb
Never mind if kittens wail——

Take a spiky little comb
To your whiskers and your tail
Take a spiky little comb
Never mind if kittens wail——

Tom   (*singing*) That's enough Mama
You're too rough Mama
That's enough Mama
Oh no more no more

That's enough Mama
You're too rough Mama
That's enough Mama
Oh no more no more.
(*Speaking*) That comb scratched me. Well, I'll scratch back.

Tom scratches Tabitha. Shocked, she licks her paw

Tabitha Tom Kitten, you should be ashamed of yourself. Come, Moppet
and Mittens—put on your nice clean pinafores and tuckers.

Moppet and Mittens start to struggle reluctantly into these clothes

Now Thomas, I have all sorts of elegant clothes to dress you up in.

Tom But I don't want to be dressed. All clothes are uncomfortable. And elegant clothes are the worst of all.

Tabitha (*pushing him into his suit*) You shall wear your sky-blue suit. Hold out your arms. Breathe in, Thomas. Oh dear. There goes a button. Oh, another one's burst off. Stand still, I must sew them on. You burst all your buttons.

Tom I've grown, mama.

Mittens
Moppet } (*together*) He's a very fat kitten.

Tom No, I'm not.

Tabitha Hold still, or my needle is sure to jab you. There! You're done. Now all three of you are beautiful. But I want you all to be out of the way while I make hot buttered toast. Out you go, into the garden! (*She pushes them out into the garden, then peeps out, toasting-fork in hand, to say*) Now keep your frocks clean, children! You must walk on your hind legs. Keep away from the dirty ash-pit, and from Sally Henny Penny and from the pigsty. And don't have anything to do with the Puddle-Ducks.

Mittens We'd better walk carefully.

Moppet Why don't we sing our garden song?

Walking unsteadily the Kittens sing, together with the audience

                                    We Have a Little Garden
Kittens   We have a little garden
                                    A garden of our own
                                    And every day we water there
                                    The seeds that we have sown

                                    We love our little garden
                                    And tend it with such care
                                    You will not find a faded leaf
                                    Or blighted blossom there

                                    We have a little garden
                                    A garden of our own
                                    And every day we water there
                                    The seeds that we have sown

                                    We love our little garden
                                    And tend it with such care

You will not find a faded leaf
Or blighted blossom there.

Bright snowdrops in the winter
And Christmas roses there
Then springtime brings the crocuses
To sniff the April air

The pears and apples shining
They cheer us in the fall
But strawberries mean summertime
The sweetest time of all.

Mittens and Moppet tread on their pinafores and fall on their noses. When they stand up they are smeared with green cut grass. Tom is trying to catch a butterfly

Moppet Let us climb up the rockery and sit on the garden wall.

Mittens and Moppet turn their pinafores back to front and skip and jump up the rockery. Moppet's white tucker falls into the lane. Tom tries to jump after them, but it's difficult

Beatrix Potter Tom Kitten was quite unable to skip and jump like his sisters when walking upon his hind legs. He came up the rockery by degrees, breaking the ferns, and shedding buttons right and left.

Tom reaches the top of the wall and is inspected by Mittens and Moppet

Moppet Oh Tom, you're all in pieces.
Mittens Let's try to pull him together.

They try. Tom's hat falls off into the lane

Tom It's not working. There go the rest of my kitten buttons.

As they struggle, the three Puddle-Ducks come marching up the lane. They are large and white and intimidating for the kittens

Pit Pat Paddle Pat

Ducks   Pit pat paddle pat!
                     Pit pat waddle pat!
Drake   I'm Drake Puddle-Duck.

Ducks	Pit pat paddle pat!
Rebeccah	I'm Rebeccah Puddle-Duck.
Ducks	Pit pat waddle pat!
Jemima	I'm Jemima Puddle-Duck.
Ducks	We are the Puddle-Ducks.
	Pit pat paddle pat!
	Pit pat waddle pat!

The Ducks stop and stand in a row, staring up at the Kittens on the wall

Rebeccah Here's a pretty tucker. (*She picks up Moppet's tucker and puts it on*)

Jemima Here's a fine hat. (*She puts on Tom's hat*)

The Kittens start laughing and pushing each other. They fall off the wall and the rest of Tom's clothes come off

Mittens Tom Kitten! Look—all your clothes have come off!

Moppet Come! Mr Drake Puddle-Duck. Come and help us to dress him! Come and button up Tom!

Drake advances sideways towards Tom's clothes and picks them up and examines them

Drake (*putting them on himself*) Sky-blue ... sky-blue. An excellent colour. Very suitable for the good old duck-pond. A very suitable sky-blue suit. (*Now he has put on Tom's clothes*) It's a very fine morning.

The Kittens climb back up on to their garden wall as the Ducks set off down the road, singing their song

Pit Pat Paddle Pat

Ducks	Pit pat paddle pat!
	Pit pat waddle pat!
	Pit pat paddle pat!
	Pit pat waddle pat!
	We are the Puddle-Ducks
	We are the Puddle-Ducks
	Pit pat paddle pat!
	Pit pat waddle pat!
	Pit pat paddle pat!
	Pit pat waddle pat!

The Ducks exit

Moppet (*shouting after them*) That jacket fits you even worse than Tom Kitten!

Tabitha emerges from the cottage

Tabitha Mittens! Moppet! Tom Kitten! Whatever do you think you're doing—sitting on the garden wall with no clothes on? (*She pulls them off the wall and cuffs them and drives them back to the cottage*) There'll be no hot buttered toast for you. My friends will arrive for tea in a minute, and you are not fit to be seen. I am affronted. Yes, I am affronted.

The kittens are shooed out of sight

What have I done to deserve such kittens? Still, the garden's looking at its best for my visitors.

We Have a Little Garden
(*She sings*) We have a little garden
A garden of our own
And every day we water there
The seeds that we have sown

We love our little garden
And tend it with such care
You will not find a failed leaf
Or blighted blossom there.

The church clock chimes four

Four o'clock. Tea-time. And here come my friends.

Her three friends, characters from other stories (see Production Notes), come into the garden. They speak in a refined fashion

Friend 1 Your garden's looking delectable, Mrs Tabitha Twitchit.
Friend 2 Your fur and whiskers were never glossier.
Friend 3 Could that be the smell of hot buttered toast?
Tabitha It could! And it is! There's hot buttered toast for everyone. (*She brings out a tray piled high with toast and tea*)

They are about to sit down when Friend 1 holds them back

Friend 1 Tabitha, where are your enchanting children?

Tabitha They're all upstairs in bed. They are unwell. They have the measles. In fact they are totally covered in spots.

Friend 3 The spots are under their fur, I suppose?

Tabitha Yes, absolutely, under their fur. Do sit down, friends. It doesn't do to keep hot buttered toast a-waiting.

Tabitha and Friends sit down to tea

Beatrix Potter So Tabitha Twitchit chatted with her friends. But I'm afraid her kittens were not in bed, not in the least. Somehow there were very extraordinary noises from the cottage bedroom, which disturbed the dignity and repose of the tea-party.

Kittens   (*off stage*) Pit pat paddle pat!
                      Are you a duck or are you a cat?
                      Do you miaow or do you quack?

Tom   (*off*) Not a cat or a duck, I'm neither of those
                      I'm Tom Kitten, the kitten who lost his clothes!

Tabitha and her friends look shocked. Beatrix Potter comes forward

Beatrix Potter As for the Puddle-Ducks, they went into a pond. The clothes all came off directly, because there were no buttons. You have seen ducks diving their heads down into the water, leaving their tails sticking up behind them? That's Mr Drake Puddle-Duck, and Jemima and Rebeccah. They have been looking for those clothes ever since the day of The Tale of Tom Kitten.

Reprise of Songs

Company   (*singing*) Pit pat paddle pat!
                      Pit pat waddle pat!
                      Pit pat paddle pat!
                      Pit pat waddle pat!
                      Are you a duck or a cat?
                      Do you miaow or do you quack?
                      Pit pat paddle pat!
                      Pit pat waddle pat!
                      Pit pat paddle pat!
                      Pit pat waddle pat!

                      Appley Dapply, a little brown mouse
                      Goes to the cupboard in somebody's house
                      Appley Dapply has sharp little eyes,
                      And Appley Dapply is so fond of pies!

In somebody's cupboard
There's everything nice,
Cake, cheese, jam, biscuits——
All charming for mice!

Appley Dapply has sharp little eyes,
And Appley Dapply is so fond of pies!

Mister Mouse, Mister Mouse
Hurry out of my house!
Mister Mouse, Mister Mouse
Scurry out of my house!

Mister Mouse, Mister Mouse
Hurry out of my house!
Mister Mouse, Mister Mouse
Scurry out of my house!

Two bad mice
Two bad mice
See how they run!
See how they run!
They like to visit you in the night
And try to eat everything in sight
And steal your playthings by candlelight
Those two bad, two bad mice.

I am a man with a gun gun gun
I think shooting animals is fun fun fun
If I heard a robin that sang sang sang
I'd stop his singing with my bang bang bang
For I think shooting animals is fun fun fun
And I am a man with a gun gun gun
Yes I am a man with a gun

I am a man with a gun gun gun
I think shooting animals is fun fun fun
If I heard a robin that sang sang sang
I'd stop his singing with my bang bang bang
For I think shooting animals is fun fun fun
And I am a man with a gun gun gun
Yes I am a man with a gun

Carrot so crunchy
And orangey red

Carrot from somebody's
Vegetable bed!

Carrot so juicy
Carrot so fine,
Oh, how I love you
Carrot of mine!

Carrot so crunchy
And orangey red
Carrot from somebody's
Vegetable bed!

Carrot so juicy
Carrot so fine,
Oh, how I love you
Carrot of mine!

Carrot so crunchy
And orangey red
Carrot from somebody's
Vegetable bed!

Carrot so juicy
Carrot so fine,
Oh, how I love you
Carrot of mine!

Beatrix Potter Thank you for coming to the theatre today and listening to Beatrix Potter's stories of Tom Kitten and His Friends. We hope you enjoyed them and will read them for yourself, the books she made for you. Goodbye!

Company

We have a little garden
A garden of our own
And every day we water there
The seeds that we have sown

We love our little garden
And tend it with such care
You will not find a faded leaf
Or blighted blossom there
Or blighted blossom there

THE END

FURNITURE AND PROPERTY LIST

Further dressing may be added at the director's discretion

ACT I

On stage: Piano. *On it:* candles in brackets
Wicker basket containing long skirt, jacket, hat, rabbit puppet with
collar and light lead

THE STORY OF MISS MOPPET

On stage: Cupboard
Fireplace
Bell-pull
Cushion
Huge blue and white duster

Personal: **Mouse:** hand-puppet

THE TALE OF TWO BAD MICE

On stage: Stairs
Large doll's pram
Large box marked "provisions", containing wood shavings, dishes,
and food models: 2 red lobsters, ham, fish, pudding, pears, oranges
Kitchen table
Clock
Knife and fork
Tin spoon
Fire-tongs
Shovel
Fireplace containing "red-hot" crinkly paper fire
Canisters
Beads
Chest of drawers containing Jane's clothes
Bolster

Book
Birdcage
Iron
Looking-glass
Cradle on rockers
Chair
Coverlet
Broom
Model baby mouse
Cradle containing three model baby mice

Off stage: Doll's house, doll Jane, doll Lucinda (**Assistant**)
Stockings (**Dolls**)

Personal: **Tom Thumb:** sixpence

ACT II

On stage: Piano containing rabbit puppet as in Act I

Personal: **Beatrix Potter:** hat

THE STORY OF A FIERCE BAD RABBIT

On stage: Green bench
Painted trees

Off stage: Carrot (**Nice**)
Shotgun, green hat, bag for game (**Man**)

Personal: **Fierce:** tail, whiskers

THE TALE OF TOM KITTEN

On stage: Wash basin
Towels
Sponge
Brush
Comb
Clothes

Off Stage: Tray piled high with toast and tea (**Tabitha**)

LIGHTING PLOT

Property fittings required: nil
3 interior and 2 exterior settings

ACT I

To open: Overall general lighting

*No cue*s

ACT I, THE STORY OF MISS MOPPET

To open: Change lighting

*No cue*s

ACT I, THE TALE OF TWO BAD MICE

To open: Overall general lighting

Cue 1   **Beatrix Potter** plays the piano   (Page 8)
              Change lighting

Cue 2   **Lucinda**: "What a beautiful evening!"   (Page 9)
              Fade lights somewhat

Cue 3   **Jane**: "And just look at the moon and stars."   (Page 9)
              Bring up starry sky with moonlight

Cue 4   **Beatrix Potter** lights candles   (Page 9)
              Back up candlelight

Cue 5   **Beatrix Potter** plays piano   (Page 15)
              Bring up house lights

ACT II

To open: Overall general lighting

*No cue*s

ACT II, The Story of a Fierce Bad Rabbit

To open: Overall general lighting

Cue 6   **Man** fires shotgun   (Page 21)
           Wild lighting effect

ACT II, The Tale of Tom Kitten

To open: Overall general lighting

*No cue*s

EFFECTS PLOT

ACT I

Cue 1   **Lucinda**: "We are invited for six o'clock."   (Page 9)
Clock strikes six

ACT II

Cue 2   **Man**: "Goodbye funny bird!"   (Page 21)
Fire shotgun, not too violently

Cue 3   **Tabitha**: "Or blighted blossom there."   (Page 28)
Church clock chimes four